The Visitation of
St. Mary and St. Elisabeth

And it came to pass, that, when Elisabeth heard the saluta-
tion of Mary, the babe leaped in her womb. (St. Luke 1: 41)

Woodcut from the
Geistliche Auslegung des Lebens Jesu Christi,
published by Johann Zainer, Ulm, 1485.

CHRISTMAS
GREETINGS

The Christ Child in the Manger

And she brought forth her firstborn son, and wrapped him in swaddling clothes, and laid him in a manger; because there was no room for them in the inn. (St. Luke 2: 7)

Woodcut from the
Boek van der bedroffenisse vnde herteleyde Marien,
published by Johannes Grashove, Magdeburg, 1486.

CHRISTMAS
GREETINGS

The Holy Family in Bethlehem

And she brought forth her firstborn son, and wrapped him in swaddling clothes, and laid him in a manger; because there was no room for them in the inn. (St. Luke 2: 7)

Woodcut from the
Boek van der bedroffenisse vnde herteleyde Marien,
published by Johannes Grashove, Magdeburg, 1486.

CHRISTMAS
GREETINGS

The Annunciation to the Shepherds

And there were in the same country shepherds abiding in the field ... And, lo, the angel of the Lord came upon them. (St. Luke 2: 8, 9)

Woodcut from the
Spiegel menschlicher Behaltnis,
published by Peter Drach, Speyer, 1500.

CHRISTMAS
GREETINGS

The Shepherds Arrive at the Manger

The shepherds said one to another, Let us now go even unto Bethlehem . . . And they came with haste, and found Mary, and Joseph, and the babe lying in a manger. (St. Luke 2: 15, 16)

Woodcut from the
Geistliche Auslegung des Lebens Jesu Christi,
published by Johann Zainer, Ulm, 1485.

CHRISTMAS
GREETINGS

The Shepherds with the
Holy Family at the Manger

The shepherds said one to another, Let us now go even
unto Bethlehem ... And they came with haste, and found
Mary, and Joseph, and the babe lying in a manger. (St.
Luke 2: 15, 16)

Woodcut from the
Boek der Episteln unde Evangelien,
Lübeck, 1492.

CHRISTMAS
GREETINGS

The Wise Men Visit King Herod

In the days of Herod the king, behold, there came wise men from the east to Jerusalem, saying, Where is he that is born King of the Jews? (St. Matthew 2: 1, 2)

Woodcut from the
Geistliche Auslegung des Lebens Jesu Christi,
published by Johann Zainer, Ulm, 1485.

CHRISTMAS
GREETINGS

The Wise Men See the Star

In the days of Herod the king, behold, there came wise
men from the east to Jerusalem, saying, Where is he that
is born King of the Jews? for we have seen his star in the
east, and are come to worship him. (St. Matthew 2: 1, 2)

Woodcut from the
Speculum humanae salvationis,
published by Bernhard Richel, Basel, 1476.

CHRISTMAS
GREETINGS

The Wise Men Sent by
Herod to Find the Holy Child

When they had heard the king, they departed; and, lo, the
star, which they saw in the east, went before them, till it
came and stood over where the young child was. (St.
Matthew 2 : 9)

Woodcut from the
Buch der Heiligen drei Könige
by Johannes Hildeshemiensis,
published by Johann Prüss, Strasbourg, ca. 1500.

CHRISTMAS GREETINGS

The Adoration of the Wise Men

They saw the young child with Mary his mother, and fell
down, and worshipped him. (St. Matthew 2: 11)

Woodcut from the
Cronica van der hilliger Stat van Coellen,
published by Johann Koelhoff the Younger, Cologne, 1499.

CHRISTMAS
GREETINGS

The Gifts of the Wise Men

And when they had opened their treasures, they presented
unto him gifts; gold, and frankincense, and myrrh. (St.
Matthew 2: 11)

Woodcut from the
Geistliche Auslegung des Lebens Jesu Christi,
published by Johann Zainer, Ulm, 1485.

CHRISTMAS
GREETINGS

The Holy Family at Home

And when eight days were accomplished . . . his name was
called JESUS. (St. Luke 2: 21)

Woodcut from the
Boek der Episteln unde Evangelien,
Lübeck, 1492.

CHRISTMAS GREETINGS

The Presentation of Jesus in the Temple

They brought him to Jerusalem, to present him to the Lord.
(St. Luke 2: 22)

Woodcut from the
Spiegel menschlicher Behaltnis,
published by Peter Drach, Speyer, 1500.

CHRISTMAS
GREETINGS

The Angel Tells
Joseph to Flee into Egypt

The angel of the Lord appeareth to Joseph in a dream,
saying, Arise, and take the young child and his mother,
and flee into Egypt. (St. Matthew 2: 13)

Woodcut from the
Itinerarium Beatae Mariae Virginis,
published by Lienhart Ysenhut, Basel, ca. 1489.

CHRISTMAS
GREETINGS

The Holy Family
on the Flight into Egypt

When he arose, he took the young child and his mother by
night, and departed into Egypt. (St. Matthew 2: 14)

Woodcut from the
Spiegel menschlicher Behaltnis,
published by Peter Drach, Speyer, 1500.

CHRISTMAS
GREETINGS